Bob Bug has a big pan and a lot of tins.

Bob cuts up a bun.

Bob tips in a pot of jam.

Bob cuts up a lemon, a melon and a fig.

Mix, mix, mix!
Bob rubs his tum.

Bob tips in a lot of nuts.
Mix, mix, mix!

Dad Bug says, "Yuk!"
Mum Bug says, "Yuk!"

But Bob Bug says, "Yum yum!"